Literacy
BASICS

FOR AGES 5-6 KEY STAGE 1

Contents

Ways to help your child at home

Introduction

Basic literacy in the early years involves *letters, sounds* and *words*. The following are some simple, everyday activities which you can do at home which will help your child's understanding in these areas.

Activities to help with letter formation

These activities will help with your child's coordination generally:

- play threading activities with beads, buttons and laces
- make things with Play Doh
- do jigsaw puzzles
- play with construction toys (like Lego)
- try any cutting and sticking activities.

When helping your child write letter shapes, concentrate on lower case (small) letters and not capitals. Always encourage your child to begin each letter in the correct place and form the letter in the way shown in the book.

Activities for teaching letter sounds

- play 'I Spy' using the letter sound (e.g. 'buh' not 'bee')
- have fun with sentences and rhymes where all the words begin with the same letter. (For example, say tongue twisters like 'Peter Piper picked a peck of pickled peppers')
- make some simple post boxes out of cereal packets
  - label each with a different letter
  - cut out pictures of things beginning with different letters and post them in the correct boxes
- have fun with rhyming. Think of a short word and encourage your child to think up other words that rhyme with it, for example, sun, bun, fun, run
- read lots of nursery rhymes together.

Activities for teaching words

- make large name cards for the family, toys, pets, etc. Give your child separate copies of them to match with the original set. Encourage your child to trace or copy them
- make labels for things in your house, e.g. the table, chair, television. Stick them on the appropriate object. Provide copies of them for matching
- make, and read together, simple captions under family photos in the photograph album
- take labels containing names of products from tins and packets when you go shopping
- look out for the same names in the supermarket. Encourage your child to help 'write' your shopping list with you.

The alphabet

Look and learn

All **words** are made up of **letters**.
There are **26** letters in the **alphabet**.

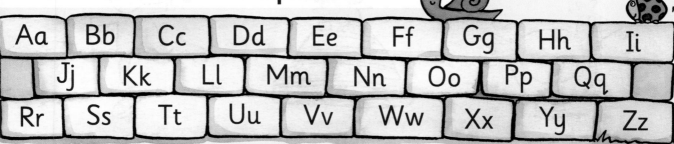

Aa	Bb	Cc	Dd	Ee	Ff	Gg	Hh	Ii
Jj	Kk	Ll	Mm	Nn	Oo	Pp	Qq	
Rr	Ss	Tt	Uu	Vv	Ww	Xx	Yy	Zz

Practice

Fill in the missing letters.

Challenge

1. Which letter comes **after** each of these?

    d___   g___   k___   n___   q___   t___

2. Which letter comes **between** each of these?

    b___d   h___j   o___q   s___u   v___x   x___z

3. Which letter comes **before** each of these?

    ___c   ___f   ___n   ___r   ___t   ___x

Look and learn

Say these words. Listen to the sound of the **first letter** of each word. The first letter is the **same**.

hen   **h**at   **h**op

Practice

Choose the first letter for each word.

m	p	h	s	h	w	d	l	p	t
_mug	__ad	__en	__og	__in

h	l	p	r	t	m	c	h	s	b
__id	__an	__op	__at	__un

Challenge

Write the words you made above.

h words	hen	hat
l words		
m words		
p words		
s words		

Make some words (2)

Look and learn

We use **letters** to make **words**.

h + a + t = hat

Practice

Finish these word sums.

c + a + t

_____cat_____

p + e + n

_____

t + i + n

_____

c + o + t

_____

b + u + n

_____

p + o + t

_____

r + u + n

_____

m + a + t

_____

h + e + n

_____

b + i + n

_____

Challenge

Write the pairs of words from above that rhyme.

at words	_____cat_____	_____mat_____
en words	_____	_____
in words	_____	_____
ot words	_____	_____
un words	_____	_____

Labels

Look and learn

Many pictures have **labels** to help you.

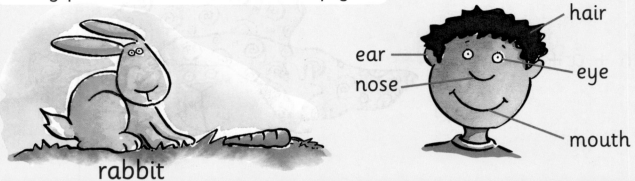

rabbit

ear — nose — hair — eye — mouth

Practice

Join the correct label to each picture.

bat ○	bee ○
cat ○	cow ○
dog ○	duck ○
horse ○	hen ○

1 2 3 4
5 6 7 8

Challenge

Finish the labels.

leg
hand
nose
foot
hair
arm

h_____
a_____
l_____
n_____
h_____
f_____

Sentences

Look and learn

A sentence should make **sense**.

can run I ☒   I can run. ☑

Practice

Write the words in order. Make some sentences.

1. can hop. I   _____ I can hop. _____
2. dog A barks.   _____
3. Fish swim. can   _____
4. cat milk. A likes   _____
5. is hot. The sun   _____
6. sun The yellow. is   _____
7. sky The blue. is   _____
8. read. can I   _____

Challenge

Make up some sentences about yourself.

1. My name is _____ .
2. I am _____ .
3. I live in _____ .
4. I can _____ .
5. I like _____ .
6. I go to _____ .

Draw yourself.

Look and learn

A **sentence** should make **sense**.

A barks. ☒   A dog barks. ☑

Practice

Choose the best word to finish each sentence.

drum   bike   sea   cake

frog   snake   bird   cow

1. You ride a _____.

2. You bang a _____.

3. You swim in the _____.

4. You eat a _____.

5. A _____ hisses.

6. A _____ sings.

7. A _____ moos.

8. A _____ hops.

Challenge

Think of a good word to finish each sentence.

1. I live in a _____.

2. You can fly in a _____.

3. Monkeys climb _____.

4. Grass is _____.

5. You read a _____.

6. You _____ a door.

Last letters

Look and learn

Say these words. Listen to the sound of the **last letter** of each word. The last letter is the **same**.

mu**g**

do**g**

ba**g**

Practice

Choose the missing letter for each word.

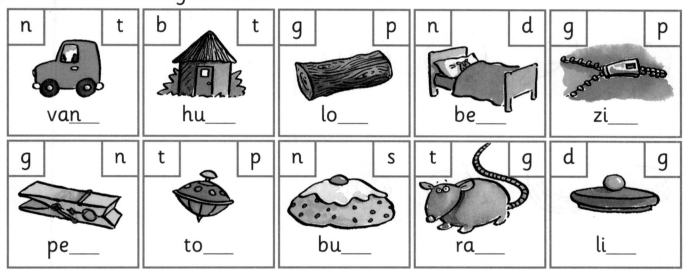

n	t	b	t	g	p	n	d	g	p
van_		hu__		lo__		be__		zi__	

g	n	t	p	n	s	t	g	d	g
pe__		to__		bu__		ra__		li__	

Challenge

Write the pairs of words you made above.

words that end with **n**	____van____	____bun____
words that end with **p**	_____	_____
words that end with **g**	_____	_____
words that end with **t**	_____	_____
words that end with **d**	_____	_____

Groups of words

Look and learn

We sometimes **group** words together.
These are all **flowers**.

daisy

buttercup

bluebell

Practice

Sort these things into two groups.

apple

carrot

cabbage

orange

potato

banana

onion

grapes

fruit	vegetables
apple	

Challenge

Write the names of four animals in each list:

wild animals	farm animals	pet animals

10

Word building

Look and learn

We can **build** words from **letters** and **groups of letters**.

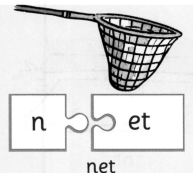 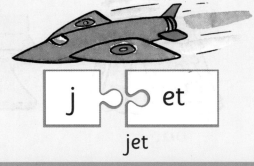 

n	et		j	et		w	et

net   jet   wet

Practice

Make these words.

b ag	h en	p in	l og	c up

____bag____ _____ _____ _____ _____

r ag	p en	b in	f og	p up

_____ _____ _____ _____ _____

Challenge

Label the pictures with the words you made above.

1.  pin	2. 	3. 	4. 	5. 
6. 	7. 	8. 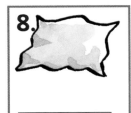	9. 	10. 

Look and learn

Say these words. Listen to the sound of the **middle letter** of each word. The middle letter is the **same**.

| cap | bag | mat |

Practice

Choose the middle letter for each word.

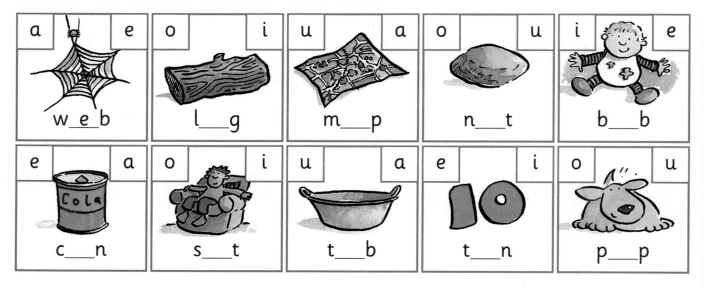

a e o	i u a	o u i	e
w _e_ b	l __ g	m __ p	n __ t	b __ b

e a o	i u a	e i o	u
c __ n	s __ t	t __ b	t __ n	p __ p

Challenge

Write the words you made above in the correct column.

a words	**e** words	**i** words	**o** words	**u** words
map can				

Capital letters and full stops

Look and learn

The boy fell in the mud.

A **sentence** begins with a **capital letter** and ends with a **full stop**.

Practice

Write these sentences correctly.

1. the car was red _____
2. a frog can hop _____
3. my apple is sweet _____
4. milk is white _____
5. all birds have wings _____
6. you kick a ball _____
7. we like to read _____
8. we are going home _____

Challenge

Match up the beginning and ending of each sentence. Write it correctly.

1. the lady bakes	football	_____
2. you dig	a picture	_____
3. we can play	a cake →	The lady bakes a cake.
4. the boy fell	a dog	_____
5. the girl draws	a song	_____
6. you sing	a hole	_____
7. you pat	my hair	_____
8. I brush	off the wall	_____

Look and learn

Some words end with **double letters**.

Hiss!

hi**ll**

hi**ss**

Practice

Make some words.

t

p

f ——— ill

m

w

till

_____

_____

_____

_____

b

l

m ——— oss

t

cr

boss

_____

_____

_____

_____

Challenge

Sort these words into sets.

yell	less	ball	miss	
tell	bell	mess	wall	
hall	hiss	call	well	

all words	**ell** words	**ess** words	**iss** words
ball			

The letters ck

Look and learn

Many words end in **ck**.

so**ck**

du**ck**

Practice

Do these word sums.

1. s + a + ck = <u> sack </u>
2. p + a + ck = _____
3. d + e + ck = _____
4. p + e + ck = _____
5. s + i + ck = _____
6. k + i + ck = _____
7. r + o + ck = _____
8. s + o + ck = _____
9. d + u + ck = _____
10. s + u + ck = _____

Challenge

Use the words you made above to complete these sentences.

1. When you are not well you feel _____.
2. A hen can _____.
3. A _____ says quack.
4. You can _____ a ball.
5. A ship has a _____.
6. A _____ is a big stone.
7. You _____ a sweet.
8. You _____ your clothes in a case.
9. My _____ has a hole in it.
10. Father Christmas carries a _____.

The letters ng and nk

Look and learn

Many words end in **ng** and **nk**.

The ki**ng** can wi**nk**.

Practice

Join up the rhyming words.

1. sing   gang   _____
2. bang   pink   _____
3. gong   rung   _____
4. hung   king → _____ sing   king _____
5. bank   sunk   _____
6. wink   song   _____
7. bunk   tank   _____

Challenge

Find the **ng** and **nk** words hidden in the flags.

b w i n g c

____wing____

d f y a n k

_____

h a n g j k

_____

l i n k m o

_____

p q r a n g

_____

s t b u n k

_____

l o n g w x

_____

h u n k z y

_____

e f b u n g

_____

16

Letter blends at the beginning of words

Look and learn

Say the words slowly. Listen to the way each word **begins**.

slip   **fl**ag   **cl**ock   **bl**ot   **gl**ass

Practice

Make these words.

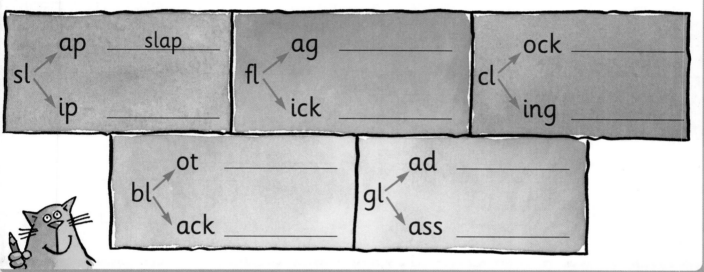

sl → ap   _slap_
sl → ip   _____

fl → ag   _____
fl → ick   _____

cl → ock   _____
cl → ing   _____

bl → ot   _____
bl → ack   _____

gl → ad   _____
gl → ass   _____

Challenge

Use the words you made above. Write the word that rhymes with:

1. bag   _flag_   **2.** sing _____

3. hot _____   **4.** pass _____

5. cap _____   **6.** sick _____

7. rock _____   **8.** sad _____

9. jack _____   **10.** hip _____

Letter blends at the end of words

Look and learn

Say the words slowly. Listen to the way each word **ends**.

ho**ld**   e**lf**   mi**lk**   he**lp**   be**lt**

Practice

Make these words.

| co | ld | | e | lf | | mi | lk | | ye | lp |

_____cold_____   _____   _____   _____

| go | ld | | go | lf | | su | lk | | gu | lp |

_____   _____   _____   _____

| me | lt | | | | ki | lt |

_____   _____

Challenge

Use the words you made above to complete these sentences.

1. We get ____milk____ from cows.
2. Ice will _____ when it gets hot.
3. _____ is a sport.
4. _____ means to shout in pain.
5. _____ is worth a lot of money.
6. An _____ is a small person in fairy stories.
7. Some people _____ when they are told off.
8. A _____ is like a skirt.
9. You _____ a drink.
10. The opposite of hot is _____.

Plurals

Look and learn

Plural means when there is **more** than one.
We add **s** to many words to make them plural.

one cat

lots of cats

Practice

Write the plurals.

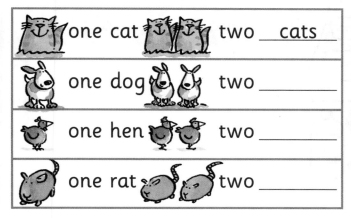

one cat — two ___cats___

one dog — two _____

one hen — two _____

one rat — two _____

one ant — two _____

one bird — two _____

one bat — two _____

one frog — two _____

Challenge

Count the spots.

one	two	three	four	five	six	seven	eight	nine	ten

1. ___three spots___

2. _____

3. _____

4. _____

5. _____

6. _____

7. _____

8. _____

9. _____

10. _____

Sets of words

Look and learn

This is a **set** of insects.

butterfly

ant

beetle

This is a **set** of birds.

robin

seagull

owl

Practice

Sort the things for the party into two sets.

cola, tea, crisps, cake, sausages, pizza, orange squash, apple juice, sandwiches, lemonade

sandwiches, apple juice, crisps, tea,
pizza, cake, cola, lemonade,
orange squash, sausages

food	drink

Challenge

Circle the odd thing out in each set.

1. cup	mug	(bike)		**2.** table	chair	bird
3. car	book	bus		**4.** mat	rabbit	mouse
5. door	pencil	pen		**6.** apple	bed	banana
7. sun	moon	tree		**8.** box	hat	coat
9. arm	leg	lorry		**10.** sea	flower	grass

Look and learn

Sentences should make **sense**.

The chair is sitting on the girl. ☒   The girl is sitting on the chair. ☑

Practice

Underline the two words in each sentence that are in the wrong place.

1. The <u>television</u> is watching the <u>girl</u>.
2. We get cows from milk.
3. The egg is eating the man.
4. The ball kicked the boy.
5. The web made a spider.
6. The tree had a garden in it.
7. The chair fell over the lady.
8. The tail had a cat.

Challenge

Write each sentence correctly.

1. A bee lives in a shell.   <u>A bee lives in a hive.</u>
2. A dog lives in a web. _____
3. A horse lives in a hive. _____
4. A spider lives in a pond. _____
5. A bird lives in a burrow. _____
6. A duck lives in a kennel. _____
7. A rabbit lives in a nest. _____
8. A snail lives in a stable. _____

The letters sh and ch

Look and learn

You will find **sh** and **ch** in many words.

ship

chest

Practice

Make some words.

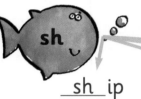

_sh_ip   _____ut   _____ed   _____op   _____ell

_____ship_____   _____   _____   _____   _____

_____ick   _____at   _____in   _____ip   _____est

_____   _____   _____   _____   _____

Challenge

Find the **sh** and **ch** words.

sh words	**ch** words
	chill

a	b	c	h	i	l	l	g
h	i	j	k	s	h	u	t
l	m	s	h	i	n	p	q
c	h	e	c	k	r	s	t
u	v	w	x	c	h	o	p
s	h	e	l	f	y	z	a
d	g	c	h	e	e	s	e
s	h	o	c	k	h	i	j
k	c	h	u	r	c	h	l
m	n	o	s	h	e	e	p

The letters ee and oo

Look and learn

The letter patterns **ee** and **oo** are two common letter patterns.

I can s**ee** the m**oo**n.

Practice

Underline the **ee** and **oo** letter patterns. Join up the rhyming words.

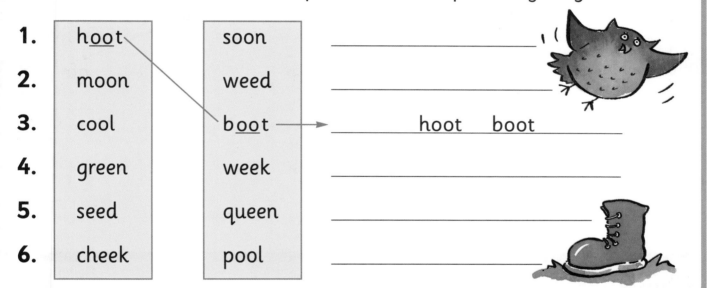

1.	h<u>oo</u>t	soon
2.	moon	weed
3.	cool	b<u>oo</u>t
4.	green	week
5.	seed	queen
6.	cheek	pool

_____

_____

_____ hoot   boot _____

_____

_____

_____

Challenge

Choose **oo** or **ee** to complete each word.

z_oo_
zoo

tr_____

st_____l

br_____m

f_____t

w_____p

r_____f

sw_____t

sl_____p

sp_____n

The letters ay and ai

Look and learn

tr**ay**

r**ai**n

The letters **ay** often come at the **end** of a word.

The letters **ai** often come in the **middle** of a word.

Practice

Make some words.

s ——— say ———

d ——— ———

w ——— **ay** ———

st ——— ———

pl ——— ———

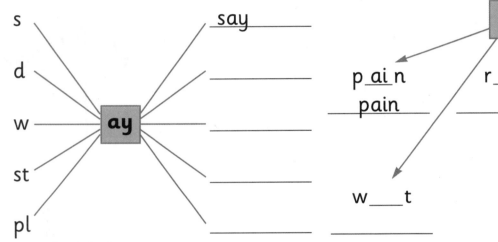

ai

p_ai_n ——— r___l ——— afr___d ———

pain ——— ——— ———

w___t ——— r___n ———

Challenge

Use the words you made above to complete these sentences.

1. It is a sunny ___day___ .

2. Tom had a _____ in his tooth.

3. I think it is going to _____ .

4. My friend came to _____ for the weekend.

5. Can you _____ what I can do?

6. I had to _____ for a bus to come.

7. Do you like to _____ football?

8. Which _____ is it to school?

9. Mr James put up a curtain _____ .

10. I am _____ of the dark.

Vowels and consonants

Look and learn

There are **26** letters of the **alphabet**. The five **vowels** are **a, e, i, o** and **u**. All the other letters are called **consonants**.

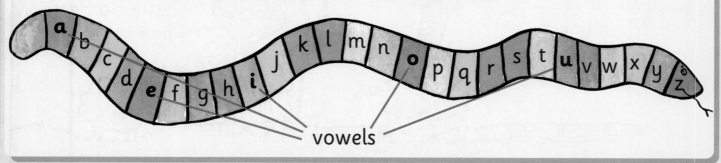

vowels

Practice

Colour the vowels red. Colour the consonants blue.

a	b	c	d	e	f	g	h	i

j	k	l	m	n	o	p	q

r	s	t	u	v	w	x	y	z

Write the vowels: _____ _____ _____ _____ _____

Challenge

Fill in the missing vowel in each word.

s_u_n
_____sun_____

c___t
_____

sh___p
_____

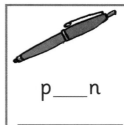

p___n
_____

t___ll
_____

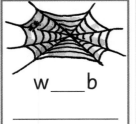

w___b
_____

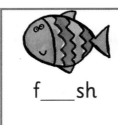

f___sh
_____

b___s
_____

cl___ck
_____

b___g
_____

Names

Look and learn

Whenever we write **someone's name** we should always **start** it with a **capital letter**.

My name is Humpty Dumpty.

My name is Little Bo Peep.

Practice

Write each child's name again correctly.

ben	yasmin	lewis	zoe	nadeen
_____	_____	_____	_____	_____

grace	mark	waka	olivia	warren
_____	_____	_____	_____	_____

Challenge

1. Write your name. _____

2. Write the names of two friends. _____

3. Write the name of an uncle or an aunt. _____

4. Write the name of your teacher. _____

5. Write the name of your doctor. _____

6. Write the name of someone famous. _____

The endings ed and ing

Look and learn

We can add the endings **ing** and **ed** to some words.

I am walk**ing** to the shops.
walk + ing = walk**ing**

Yesterday I walk**ed** to school.
walk + ed = walk**ed**

Practice

Complete this chart.

	+ing	+ed
talk	talking	talked
wash		
shout		
kick		
jump		
look		
lift		
rock		

Challenge

Take the **ing** or **ed** off each word.

1. raining _____rain_____

2. filled _____

3. called _____

4. eating _____

5. singing _____

6. licked _____

7. cooked _____

8. catching _____

9. staying _____

10. packed _____

11. opened _____

12. drawing _____

Look and learn

What is for dinner?

A **question** must begin with a **capital letter** and end with a **question mark**.

Practice

Write these questions correctly.

1. where do you live   <u>Where do you live?</u>

2. what is your name

3. how old are you

4. when is your birthday

5. where are you going

6. what is the matter

7. who are you with

8. what has happened

Challenge

Here are some answers. Write what you think the questions were.

1. <u>Who is your teacher?</u>   My teacher is Miss Jones.

2. _____ My brother is ten.

3. _____ My sister is called Sarah.

4. _____ I am seven.

5. _____ I go to Park Farm School.

6. _____ My favourite colour is red.

7. _____ I like Art best at school.

8. _____ I play with my friend after school.

Look and learn

The two letter patterns **ea** and **oa** are **common**.

r**ea**d

r**oa**d

Practice

Underline the **ea** and **oa** letter patterns. Join up the rhyming words.

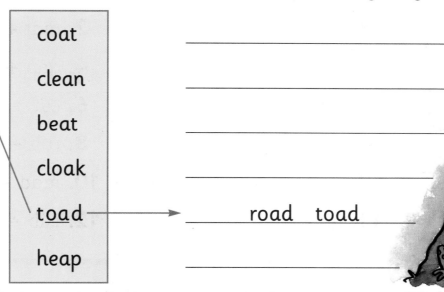

1.	road	coat	
2.	leap	clean	
3.	boat	beat	
4.	neat	cloak	
5.	mean	toad	→ road toad
6.	soak	heap	

Challenge

Choose **ea** or **oa** to complete each word.

s_ea_
sea

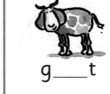

g___t

s___t

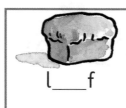

l___f

b___k

s___p

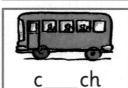

t___

c___ch

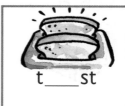

r___d

t___st

Magic e

Look and learn

Say the words. Notice what happens when we add **e**.

I hat**e** my hat!

hat – hate

I have a cap and a cap**e**.

cap – cape

Practice

Make some new words.

1. kit + e = <u>kite</u>

2. mat + e = _____

3. rip + e = _____

4. gap + e = _____

5. rob + e = _____

6. cut + e = _____

7. not + e = _____

8. tub + e = _____

9. pin + e = _____

10. mad + e = _____

11. hop + e = _____

12. cub + e = _____

Challenge

Choose the correct word

tap/tape	rid/ride	mop/mope	mat/mate	pip/pipe
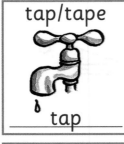				
<u>tap</u>	_____	_____	_____	_____

cub/cube	win/wine	tub/tube	shin/shine	gap/gape
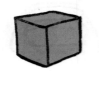				
_____	_____	_____	_____	_____

Days and months

Look and learn

There are **seven days** in a **week**.

Munday ☒   Monday ☑

There are **12 months** in a **year**.

Febuary ☒   February ☑

It is important to know how to **spell** the names of **days** and **months**.

Practice

Write the days of the week correctly in the right order.

Tuesday
Friday
Sunday
Saturday
Wednesday
Monday
Thursday

_____
_____
_____
_____
_____
_____
_____

Challenge

Here is a rhyme to help you remember how many days there are in each month.

Thirty days hath September,
April, June and November.
All the rest have thirty-one,
Except for February alone,
Which has 28 days clear,
And 29 in each leap year.

Write the names of the months correctly in order.

1. January   2. _____
3. _____   4. _____
5. _____   6. _____
7. _____   8. _____
9. _____   10. _____
11. _____   12. December

Rhyming

Look and learn

Sometimes **rhyming** words have the **same** letter patterns.

I put on the **light** in the n**ight**.

Sometimes **rhyming** words have **different** letter patterns.

That is m**y** p**ie**.

Practice

Make some pairs of rhyming words.

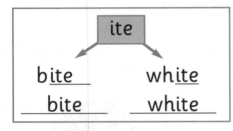

ite
b**ite**   wh**ite**
bite   _white_

y
b____   tr____
_____   _____

ie
l____   d____
_____   _____

y
fl____   cr____
_____   _____

igh
h____   s____
_____   _____

ine
f____   m____
_____   _____

Challenge

Match up the pairs of rhyming words.

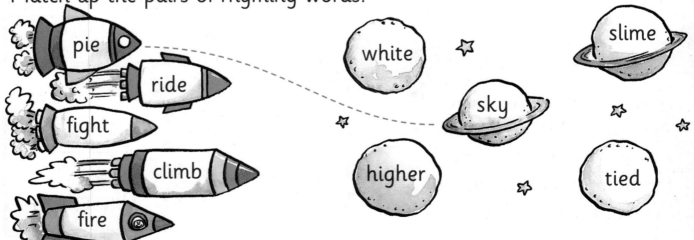

pie   ride   fight   climb   fire

white   slime   sky   higher   tied